It's Easy To Play
The Thirties.

Wise Publications
London/New York/Sydney

Exclusive Distributors:
Music Sales Limited
8/9 Frith Street, London W1V 5TZ, England
Music Sales Pty. Limited
120 Rothschild Avenue, Rosebery, NSW 2018, Australia

This book © Copyright 1988 by
Wise Publications
ISBN 0.7119.1323.4
Order No. AM 68313

Art direction by Mike Bell
Cover illustration by Paul Allen
Arranged by Frank Booth
Compiled by Peter Evans

Music Sales complete catalogue lists thousands
of titles and is free from your local music
book shop, or direct from Music Sales Limited.
Please send a cheque or Postal Order for £1.50 for postage to
Music Sales Limited, 8/9 Frith Street, London W1V 5TZ, England.

Printed in England by
Caligraving Limited, Thetford, Norfolk

An Apple For The Teacher

Words by Johnny Burke
Music by James V. Monaco

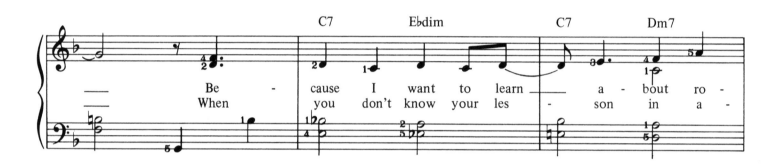

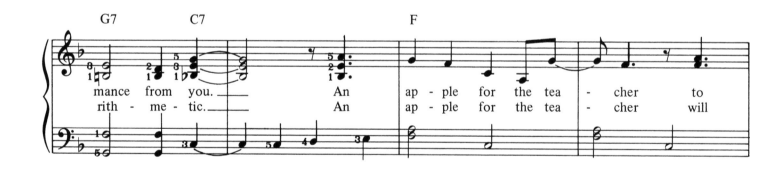

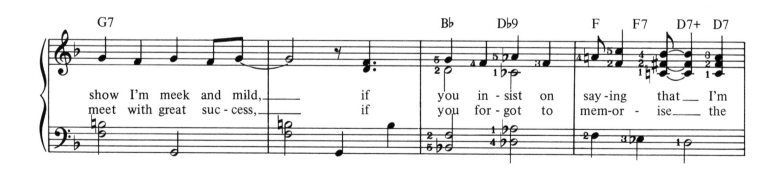

Time On My Hands

Words by Harold Adamson and Mack Gordon
Music by Vincent Youmans

Moderately

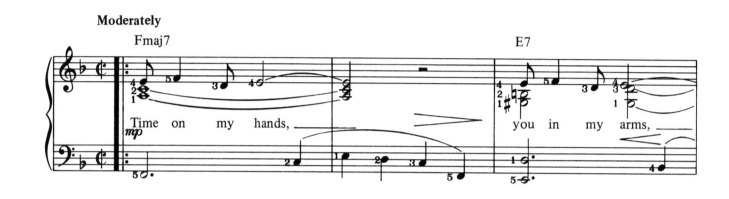

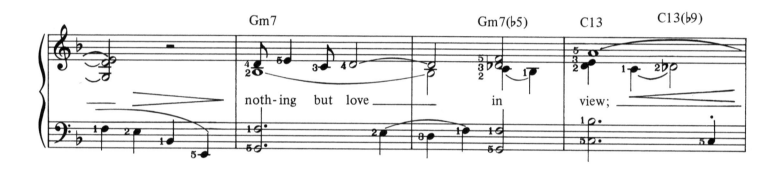

Pennies From Heaven

Words by John Burke
Music by Arthur Johnston

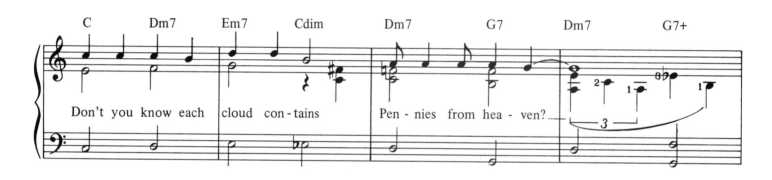

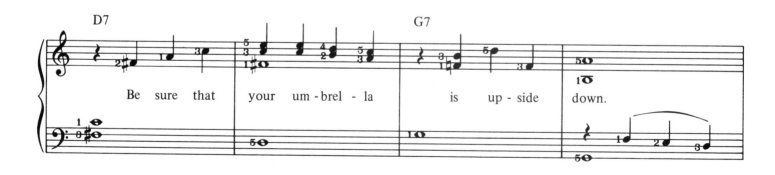

Georgia On My Mind

Words by Stuart Gorrell
Music by Hoagy Carmichael

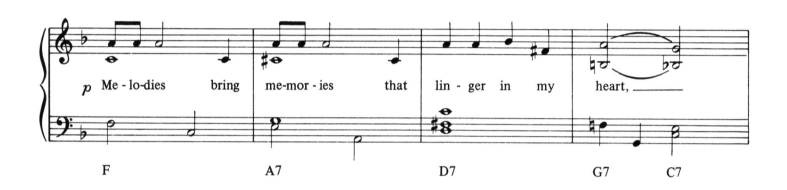

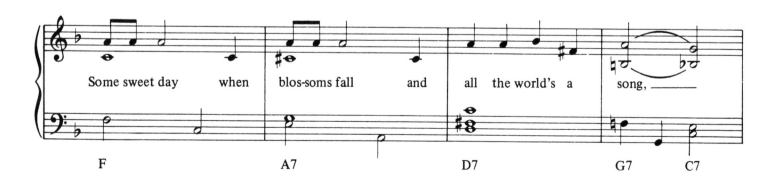

Stormy Weather

Words by Ted Koehler
Music by Harold Arlen

Just can't get my poor___ self to-geth-er___   I'm wea-ry all___ the

Am7   D9   G   Em7   Am7   D7+

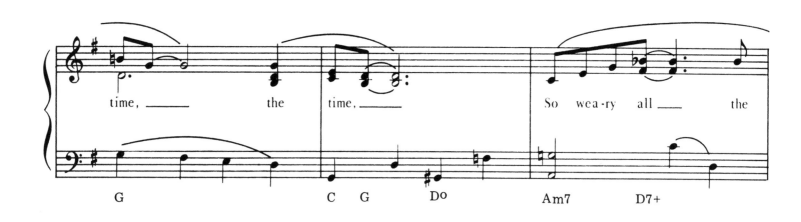

time,_____   the   time,_____   So wea-ry all___ the

G   C G   Dº   Am7   D7+

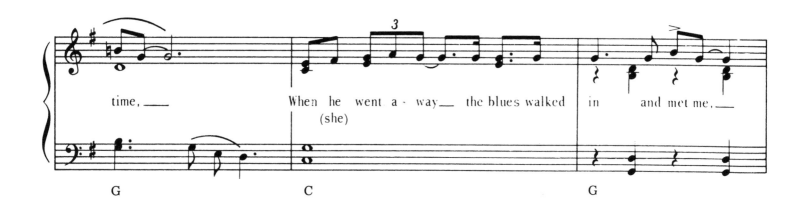

time,___   When he went a-way___ the blues walked   in   and met me,___
(she)

G   C   G

If he stays a-way___ old rock-in'   chair will get me,   all I do is pray___ the Lord a-
(she)

C   G C G C

Underneath The Arches

Words and Music by Bud Flanagan

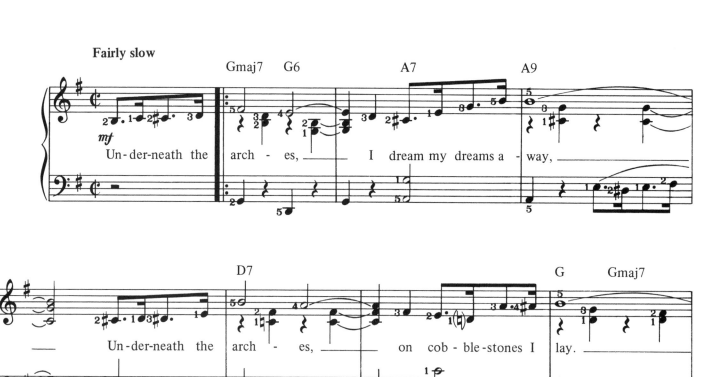

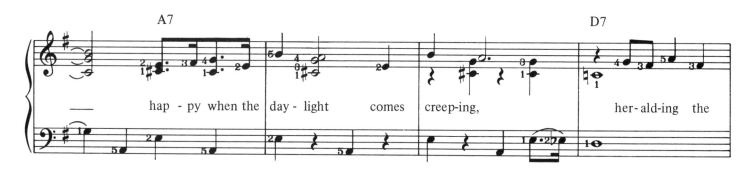

East Of The Sun
(And West Of The Moon)

Words and Music by Brooks Bowman

Stars Fell On Alabama

Words by Mitchell Parish
Music by Frank Perkins

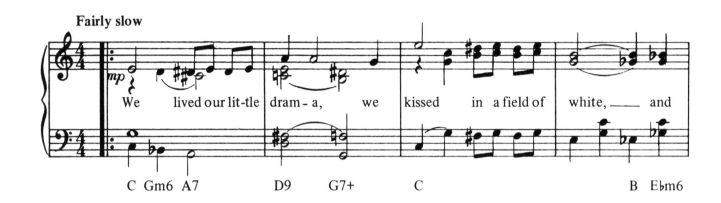

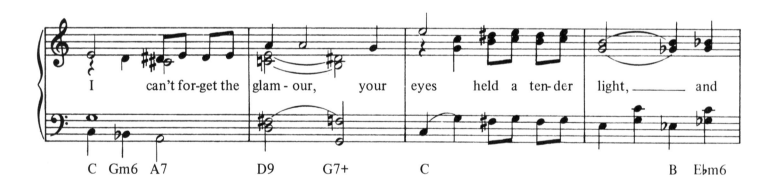

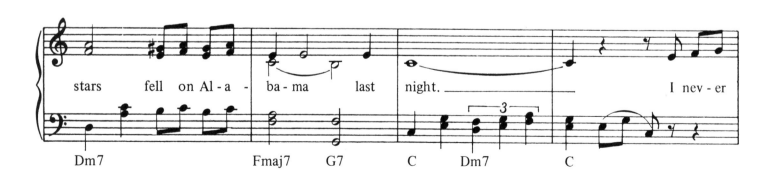

We'll Meet Again

Words and Music by Ross Parker and Hughie Charles

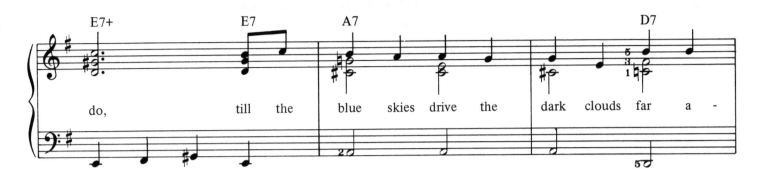

do,   till the   blue   skies   drive   the   dark   clouds   far   a -

way._____   So   will   you   please   say   "hel - lo"____   to   the

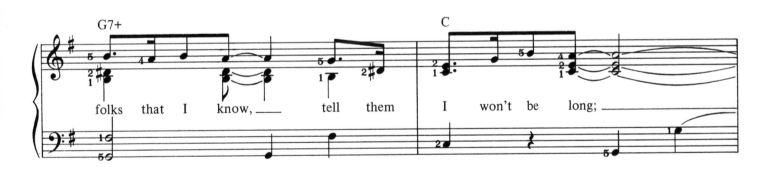

folks   that   I   know,____   tell   them   I   won't   be   long;_____

They'll   be   hap - py   to   know__   that   as   you   saw   me   go,__   I   was

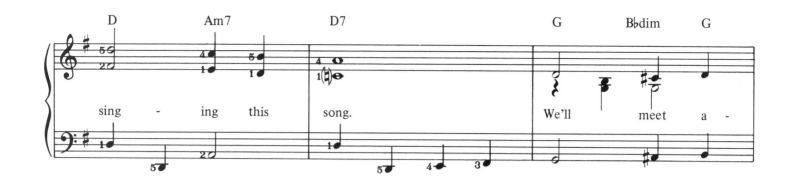

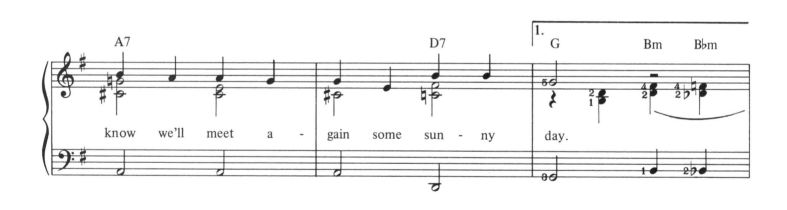

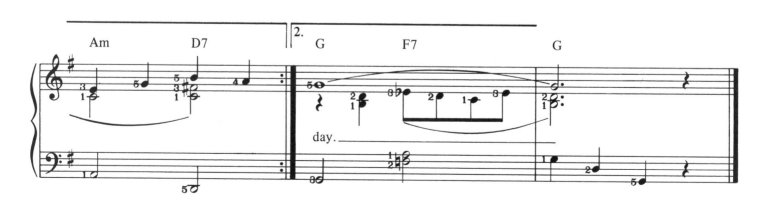

On The Sunny Side Of The Street

Words by Dorothy Fields
Music by Jimmy McHugh

with the sun in my heart, All my wor - ry blew a -
made for laugh - ter and play, If you'd have your share of

Gm7   C7   Bb7   Am7

ritard.

way when you taught me how to say:
fun, there's but one thing to be done: Grab your

D9   Dm7   G7

CHORUS

coat and get your hat, leave your wor - ry on the door - step,

C   E7   F   G6

Just dir - ect your feet to the sun - ny side of the street, Can't you

C Am7 D7   Dm7 G7 C   G7

hear a pit - ter pat? and that hap - py tune is your step? life can be so

C   E7   F   G6   C   Am7

26

I'm Gettin' Sentimental Over You

Words by Ned Washington
Music by Geo. Bassman

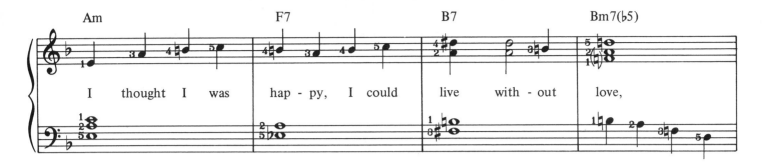

I thought I was hap-py, I could live with-out love,

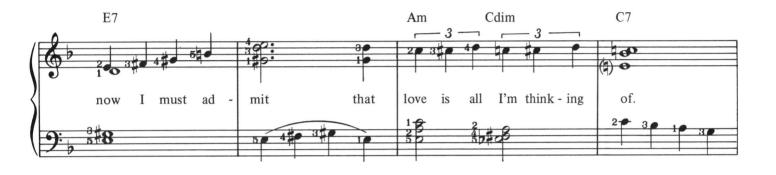

now I must ad - mit that love is all I'm think-ing of.

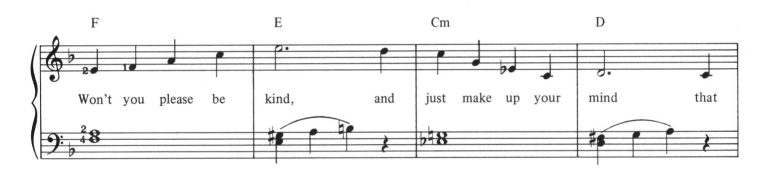

Won't you please be kind, and just make up your mind that

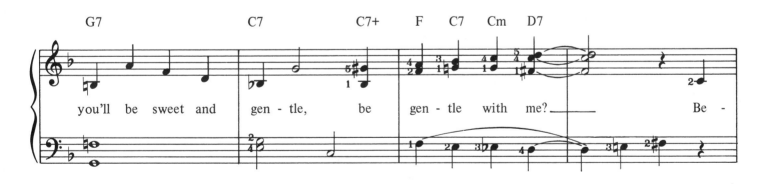

you'll be sweet and gen - tle, be gen - tle with me? Be -

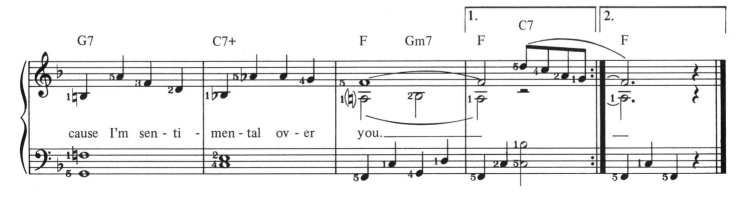

cause I'm sen - ti - men - tal ov - er you.

P.S. I Love You

Words by Johnny Mercer
Music by Gordon Jenkins

Goodnight Sweetheart

Words and Music by
Ray Noble, Jimmy Campbell and Reg Connelly

Moderately

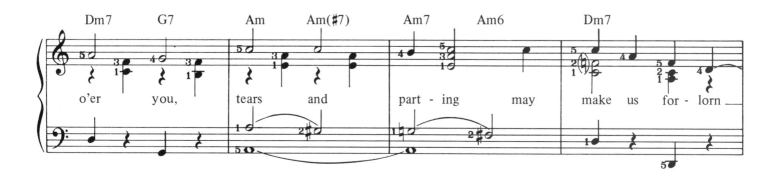

The Touch Of Your Lips

Words and Music by Ray Noble

Slowly

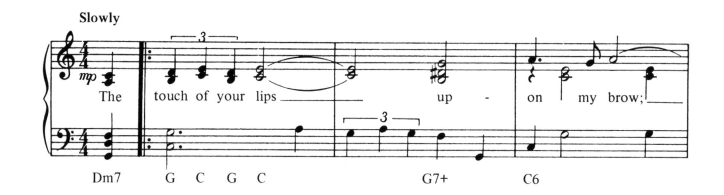

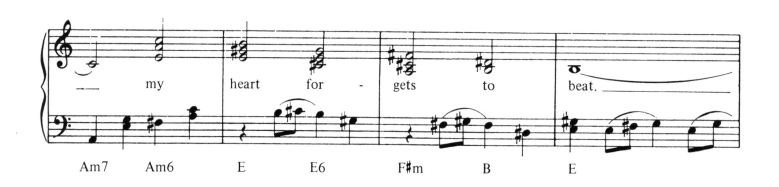

Don't Blame Me

Words and Music by Jimmy McHugh and Dorothy Fields

Don't blame me for fall-ing in love with you. I'm

un-der your spell but how can I help it, don't blame me.

Can't you see when you do the things you do, if

I can't con-ceal the thrill that I'm feel-ing, don't blame me.

Mood Indigo

Words and Music by
Duke Ellington, Irving Mills and Albany Bigard

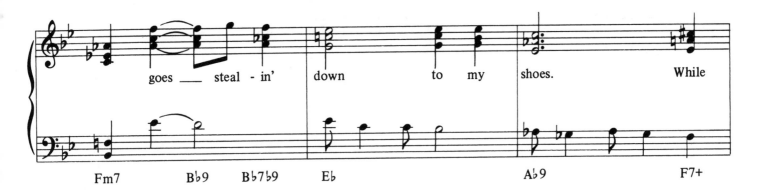

goes ___ steal - in' down to my shoes. While

Fm7   B♭9   B♭7♭9   E♭   A♭9   F7+

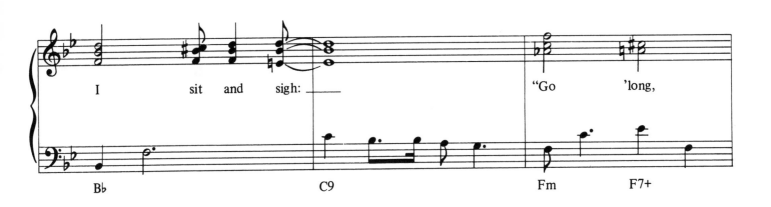

I sit and sigh: ___ "Go 'long,

B♭   C9   Fm   F7+

CHORUS

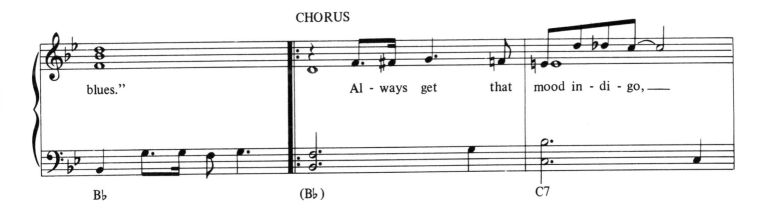

blues."   Al - ways get that mood in - di - go, ___

B♭   (B♭)   C7

Since my ba - by said good - bye, ___   In the eve - nin'

E♭   F7   B♭ Fdim F7   B♭

when lights are low, ___ I'm so lone - some I could cry.

'Cause there's no - bo - dy who cares a - bout me, ___ I'm just a soul who's

blu - er than blue ___ can be; When I get that mood in - di - go, ___

I could lay me down and die. die. ___

Try A Little Tenderness

Words and Music by
Harry Woods, Jimmy Campbell and Reg Connelly

It's not just sen-ti-men-tal, she has her grief and care, and a word _____ that's soft and gen-tle, makes it ea-si-er to bear. You won't re-gret it, wo-man don't for-get it, love is their whole hap-pi-ness. It's all so ea-sy, try a lit-tle ten-der-ness. —ness.

C7 F E7 Am A7 Dm A7 Dm Gsus G C Dm7 G7 C Gm/Bb A D7 F6 Dm7 G7 C G7 C

1 2 D.C.

43

More Than You Know

Words and Music by William Rose and Edward Eliscu
Music by Vincent Youmans

Moderato

More than you know, more than you know, "man"/"girl" o' my

heart, I love you so. Late-ly I find you're on my mind, more than you

know. Whe-ther you're right, whe-ther you're wrong, "man"/"girl" o' my

heart, I'll come a-long. You need me so, more than you'll ev-er

know. _____ Lov-ing you the way that I do, there's no-thing I can do a -

C7   F6   C   B7   Em   Am6   Bm7

bout it; _____ Lov-ing may be all you can give but hon-ey, I can't live with -

C Em   Cm6   C G   C G   A7   Am7 D7

out you. _____ Oh, how I'd cry, Oh, how I'd cry if you got

Fmaj7 G7   G7+   C6   G7+   C6   C7

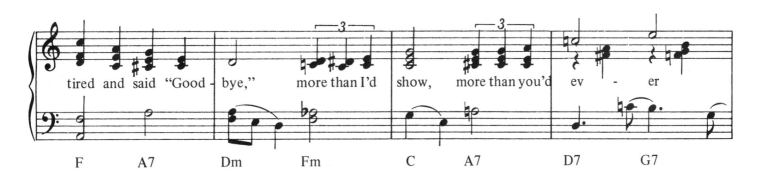

tired and said "Good-bye," more than I'd show, more than you'd ev - er

F   A7   Dm   Fm   C   A7   D7   G7

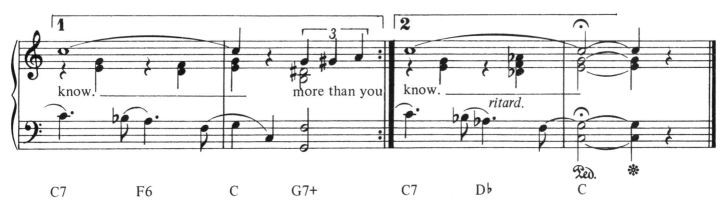

1   2
know. _____   more than you know. _____   ritard.

C7   F6   C   G7+   C7   Db   C

45

The Very Thought Of You

Words and Music by Ray Noble

Needs assessment for medical devices

WHO Medical device technical series

WHO Library Cataloguing-in-Publication Data

Needs assessment for medical devices.

(WHO Medical device technical series)

1.Appropriate technology. 2.Equipment and supplies. 3.Technology assessment, Biomedical. I.World Health Organization.

ISBN 978 92 4 150138 5   (NLM classification: WX 147)

Design & layout: L'IV Com Sàrl, Villars-sous-Yens, Switzerland.

Contents

Figures and Tables

Preface

Health technologies are essential for a functioning health system. Medical devices in particular are crucial in the prevention, diagnosis, and treatment of illness and disease, as well as patient rehabilitation. Recognizing this important role of health technologies, the World Health Assembly adopted resolution WHA60.29 in May 2007. The resolution covers issues arising from the inappropriate deployment and use of health technologies, and the need to establish priorities in the selection and management of health technologies, specifically medical devices. By adopting this resolution, delegations from Member States acknowledged the importance of health technologies for achieving health-related development goals; urged expansion of expertise in the field of health technologies, in particular medical devices; and requested that the World Health Organization (WHO) take specific actions to support Member States.

One of WHO's strategic objectives is to "ensure improved access, quality and use of medical products and technologies." This objective, together with the World Health Assembly resolution, formed the basis for establishing the Global Initiative on Health Technologies (GIHT), with funding from the Bill & Melinda Gates Foundation. GIHT aims to make core health technologies available at an affordable price, particularly to communities in resource-limited settings, to effectively control important health problems. It has two specific objectives:

- to challenge the international community to establish a framework for the development of national essential health technology programmes that will have a positive impact on the burden of disease and ensure effective use of resources;
- to challenge the business and scientific communities to identify and adapt innovative technologies that can have a significant impact on public health.

To meet these objectives, WHO and partners have been working towards devising an agenda, an action plan, tools and guidelines to increase access to appropriate medical devices. This document is part of a series of reference documents being developed for use at the country level. The series will include the following subject areas:

- policy framework for health technology
- medical device regulations
- health technology assessment
- health technology management
  - › needs assessment of medical devices
  - › medical device procurement
  - › medical equipment donations
  - › medical equipment inventory management
  - › medical equipment maintenance
  - › computerized maintenance management systems
- medical device data
  - › medical device nomenclature
  - › medical devices by health-care setting
  - › medical devices by clinical procedures
- medical device innovation, research and development.

These documents are intended for use by biomedical engineers, health managers, donors, nongovernmental organizations and academic institutions involved in health technology at the district, national, regional or global levels.

Methodology

The documents in this series were written by international experts in their respective fields, and reviewed by members of the Technical Advisory Group on Health Technology (TAGHT). The TAGHT was established in 2009 to provide a forum for both experienced professionals and country representatives to develop and implement the appropriate tools and documents to meet the objectives of the GIHT. The group has met on three occasions. The first meeting was held in Geneva in April 2009 to prioritize which tools and topics most required updating or developing. A second meeting was held in Rio de Janeiro in November 2009 to share progress on the health technology management tools under development since April 2009, to review the current challenges and strategies facing the pilot countries, and to hold an interactive session for the group to present proposals for new tools, based on information gathered from the earlier presentations and discussions. The last meeting was held in Cairo in June 2010 to finalize the documents and to help countries develop action plans for their implementation. In addition to these meetings, experts and advisers have collaborated through an online community to provide feedback on the development of the documents. The concepts were discussed further during the First WHO Global Forum on Medical Devices in September 2010. Stakeholders from 106 countries made recommendations on how to implement the information covered in this series of documents at the country level.[1]

All meeting participants and people involved in the development of these documents were asked to complete a declaration of interest form, and no conflicts were identified.

---

1   *First WHO Global Forum on Medical Devices: context, outcomes, and future actions* is available at: http://www.who.int/medical_devices/gfmd_report_final.pdf (accessed March 2011)

Definitions

Recognizing that there are multiple interpretations for the terms listed below, they are defined as follows for the purposes of this technical series.

Health technology: The application of organized knowledge and skills in the form of devices, medicines, vaccines, procedures and systems developed to solve a health problem and improve quality of life.[2] It is used interchangeably with health-care technology.

Medical device: An article, instrument, apparatus or machine that is used in the prevention, diagnosis or treatment of illness or disease, or for detecting, measuring, restoring, correcting or modifying the structure or function of the body for some health purpose. Typically, the purpose of a medical device is not achieved by pharmacological, immunological or metabolic means.[3]

Medical equipment: Medical devices requiring calibration, maintenance, repair, user training, and decommissioning – activities usually managed by clinical engineers. Medical equipment is used for the specific purposes of diagnosis and treatment of disease or rehabilitation following disease or injury; it can be used either alone or in combination with any accessory, consumable, or other piece of medical equipment. Medical equipment excludes implantable, disposable or single-use medical devices.

---

2   World Health Assembly resolution WHA60.29, May 2007 (http://www.who.int/medical_devices/resolution_wha60_29-en1.pdf, accessed March 2011).

3   Information document concerning the definition of the term "medical device". Global Harmonization Task Force, 2005 (http://www.ghtf.org/documents/sg1/sg1n29r162005.pdf, accessed March 2011).

Acknowledgements

Needs assessment for medical devices was developed under the primary authorship of Ronald Bauer, Saniplan GmbH, and under the overall direction of Adriana Velazquez-Berumen, WHO, Geneva, Switzerland as part of the Global Initiative on Health Technologies project funded by the Bill & Melinda Gates Foundation.

The document outline was reviewed by Andrew Gammie (Fishtail Consulting Ltd.) and James Wear (consultant), and the draft was reviewed by Jennifer Barragan (WHO), Adham Ismail (WHO), and was edited by Inis Communication.

We would like to thank Aditi A Sharma for assistance in proofreading and Karina Reyes-Moya and Gudrun Ingolfsdottir for administrative support throughout the development of this document.

Declarations of interests

Conflict of interest statements were collected from all contributors to and reviewers of the document. Ronald Bauer declared his employment at Saniplan GmbH, a firm that provides technical assistance and consulting services with the aim to improve the quality and accessibility of health systems and services, and Andrew Gammie his employment at Fishtail Consulting Ltd., a firm that provides advice in the area of medical devices, particularly in developing countries, as remuneration from an organization with an interest related to the subject. None of these declared conflicts influenced the content of the document.

Acronyms and abbreviations

CENETEC	Centro Nacional de Excelencia Tecnológica en Salud (National Center for Health Technology Excellence)
CMMS	computerized maintenance management system
CPG	clinical practice guidelines
GIHT	Global Initiative on Health Technologies
HIV/AIDS	human immunodeficiency virus/acquired immune deficiency syndrome
HTA	health technology assessment
HR	human resources
iHTP	Integrated Healthcare Technology Package
MoH	ministry of health
NGO	nongovernmental organization
PDSA	Plan, Do, Study, Act (prioritization matrix)
SAM	Service Availability Mapping
TAGHT	Technical Advisory Group on Health Technology
UNICEF	United Nations Children's Fund
WHO	World Health Organization

Executive Summary

Needs assessment is a complex process, incorporating a number of variables, that provides decision-makers with the information necessary to prioritize and select appropriate medical devices at a national, regional or hospital level. This document describes and illustrates the objective, the general approach and the process of such a needs assessment. The main section, *Specific approach* (Section 4), demonstrates in seven steps how to identify related needs, consider the requirements of baseline information, analyse the gathered information, appraise the options, and prioritize the specific requirements. Tools are being continuously developed to support this decision-making process, and this document also includes information on useful tools that will help in the execution of these steps.[1]

---

1   These links are also found in the section *Useful resources.*

1 Introduction

Needs assessment is a process for determining and addressing the gaps between the current situation or condition, and the desired one. It is a strategic activity and a part of the planning process that aims to improve the current performance or to correct deficiencies.

In this particular case, needs assessment is the identification and definition of prioritized requirements with regard to medical devices. A thorough needs assessment includes the potential impact on performance of medical equipment users, and on delivery of services within the context of health system capabilities and service delivery priorities. It takes into account the overall objectives of the institution, existing facilities and infrastructures, long-term plan of use, and human resources (HR) development prior to purchasing a medical device.

It is also critically important that end-users are taken into consideration and are involved in any assessment.

A needs assessment can be performed according to different scenarios and under varying circumstances. It is important to note that this activity is regularly performed as part of an effective medical equipment maintenance programme,[1] and occurs: when updating a medical equipment inventory; when re-evaluating services; and/or when replacing equipment. A needs assessment is also important prior to the construction of any new health facility.

Furthermore, it can be performed at national, regional, local or facility levels.

It should be noted that 'needs assessment of health technology' differs from 'health technology assessment' (HTA). HTA is an instrument to analyse the technical, ethical, social and economical impact, as well as the clinical effectiveness, of a specific technology.[2]

---

1 Please see *Medical equipment maintenance programme overview* in this technical series for more information.
2 Please see *Health technology assessment of medical devices* in this technical series for more information.

2 Purpose

The main objective of this document is to provide Member States with guidance for a methodological approach, as well as tools and references, and examples to conduct a proper assessment of their current situation and future needs with regard to health technologies – specifically, medical devices – in consideration of their country's health burden and disease data.

Because the characteristics of each Member State vary enormously, this document presents only generic principles. However, the resources and examples shown (or referred to) should enable any country to elaborate or adapt these principles according to their particular needs.

The document can be used for single facilities as well as for a network of facilities, up to national systems (referral systems). The tools referred to in this document do, however, need to be properly selected and appropriately applied. The ultimate goal is for countries to use the tools for integration of prioritized needs into national policies and action plans.

Note: The references and links provided are not intended to be either complete or comprehensive, but rather a selection of documents and tools identified by WHO as sources of information for decision-makers.

3 General approach

The general approach in performing a needs assessment is to examine what is available in the facility, region or country, and to compare it with what *should* be available, considering the particular demand and situation of the catchment area or target group. Part of this process includes looking at locally- and globally-recognized standards. The identified gap specifies the overall need.

By taking into consideration possible financial and HR restrictions, as well as prioritized epidemiological requirements, a list of the prioritized needs can be established. Table 1 and Figure 1 summarize and visualize the process. Table 1 specifically outlines the questions to be asked, the data required to answer those questions, and the tools available to collect and evaluate the data.

Table 1. General needs assessment approach (process)

	Questions	Data required	Tools[a]	Result
1	What do we want/need in terms of health services?	• Population (target population, catchment area) • Health service provider availability • Epidemiological data	• "Certificate of need" process, see Appendix A • Clinical practice guidelines (CPG) • Survey questionnaires • Standards of level of care • Integrated Healthcare Technology Package (iHTP)	
2	What do we have? (local conditions/ limitations)	• Health service availability • Lists of available medical devices • Human resources availability	• Service Availability Mapping (SAM) questionnaires • Evaluation manuals/tools • Inventory management tool • Computerized maintenance management system (CMMS)	
3	Which standards/ recommended best practices exist that could be applied or adapted?	• Standards/ recommendations for health service delivery coverage (catchment areas) • Standards/ recommendations for medical devices • Standards/ recommendations for human resources required for operation/maintenance/ management of medical equipment	• (essential) Medical device lists; i.e., per facility type and department, or per clinical procedure	
4=3-2	Overall gap:			List of general needs
5	What financial/human resources do we have? (constraints)	• Budget (capital investment and operational) • Human resources		
6=4-5	Prioritized needs:			Prioritized list of needs

[a] Please refer to *Useful resources* and appendices included in this document for more information on these tools.

Figure 1. General needs assessment process

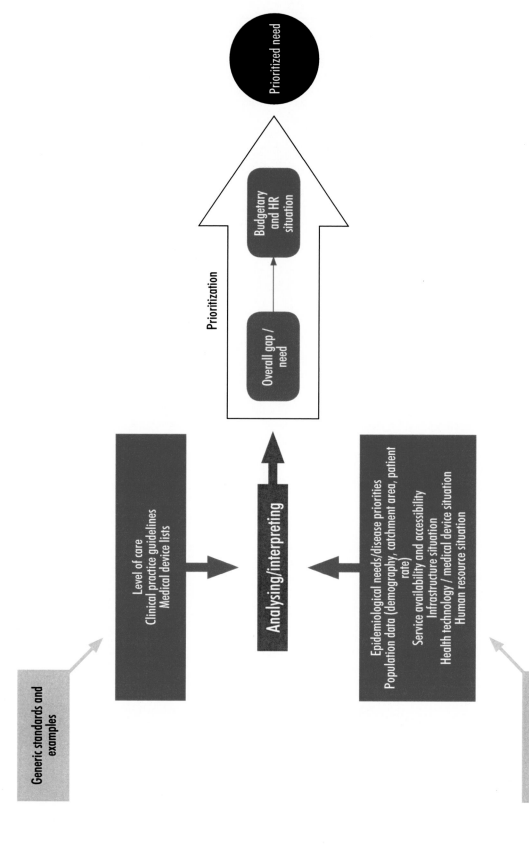

4 Specific approach

Expanding upon the general approach, this section summarizes the seven specific data collection and analysis steps of the needs assessment process. Steps I-III refer to the baseline information collection of health service requirements, health service availability, and health technology. Steps IV and V refer to the specific situation in terms of human resources and finances – and possible respective constraints – of the administration of the facility, region or state. Step VI provides suggestions for analysing and interpreting the results of Steps I-V. Lastly, Step VII briefly discusses the issue of prioritization and option appraisal.

The tables in Steps I-V also summarize what information is to be collected, the data to be considered during the collection process, and the desired result of the process. Due to the cross-cutting nature of the process, the same outcomes may be mentioned in multiple steps.

4.1   Step I: Baseline information on health service requirements

Table 2. Baseline information on health service requirements

Local geographical and public health conditions	Considerations	Result
• Population of target area, including size of the region/area, number and density of population • Major disease burden	• Epidemiological needs (disease priorities) • Population issues (demography / catchment area, patient rate) • CPG/protocols/national or local recommendations • Internationally-recognized standards on diagnosis and treatment of different diseases • Health-care issue prioritization	• Appropriate health service delivery requirements

Complete details on Step I are not provided here, as they are outside the scope of this document and the responsibility of the GIHT. However, Step I remains critically important to address, as it directly refers to the health situation of the target population.

WHO has information available at the country level while national ministries of health (MoHs) may have more detailed information.[1]

_____

1   WHO country profiles are available at http://www.who.int/countries/en

4.2   Step II: Baseline information on health service availability

Table 3. Baseline information on health service availability

Service delivery situation	Considerations	Result
• Available services (e.g., maternal and child health, HIV/AIDS, surgical, etc.) • Facilities (e.g., hospitals, clinics, etc.) • Human resources	• Health service availability and accessibility • Opinions on health service delivery from the target population • Opinions on health service delivery from service providers • Facility types, numbers, conditions • Current staffing levels	• Health service availability map (overview) • Facility map

It is important to assess the current situation in order to identify the difference between what is needed and what exists. Taking Table 3 into account, the following questions can be asked to retrieve the relevant information:

- Where is the facility(ies) located?
- Which health services are available at the facility?
- What range of clients does the facility cater to in terms of age, gender, geographical distribution, etc.?
- Which specific needs does the facility (and its services) meet?
- How does the facility receive referrals, and from whom do its referrals come?
- How many clients does the facility see each week/month/quarter/year?
- On average, how long do clients stay at the facility, and what are their reasons for leaving (e.g., drop-out, onward referral, etc.)?
- How many clients each week/month, etc., are referred on to other agencies?

- What is the caseload of staff?
- How many full-time staff does the service employ, and how much time do they have available each week for client appointments?
- Is there any information regarding staff satisfaction or facility-user satisfaction available by way of surveys?
- How do existing clients access the facility (e.g., on foot, by public transportation, etc.)?
- How accessible is the service by public transportation?

Specific tools[1] can further assist in the collection of the appropriate information for this and other steps in the process, including:

- *Service Availability Mapping (SAM)* tool, World Health Organization.
- *Rapid health facility assessment flow chart.* International Health Facility Assessment Network, 2007.

---

[1]   Reference information for these tools can be found under *Useful Resources.*

4.3 Step III: Baseline information on medical devices

Table 4. Baseline information on medical devices

Medical device situation	Considerations	Result
• Availability and condition of medical devices (including type, number, location and physical condition) • Status of electrical, water, and waste disposal systems related to medical device use	• Medical equipment inventory including status and condition • Current health technology management infrastructure (or lack thereof)	• Facility map • Medical equipment inventory (quantitative and qualitative) • Outline of health technology management infrastructure

This is the key step in the process with regard to health technology. The main goal is to identify what is available in terms of medical devices and related infrastructure, and their condition. It is important to collect as much detailed and reliable information as possible, because any change, correction or improvement will have a major impact on the financial and human resources, as well as on the environment.

A two-step approach can be followed where the first step is a neutral, quantitative assessment, and the second, a more detailed, qualitative assessment. It is up to the implementer to decide if the second step is desired or necessary.

Taking Table 4 into account, some of the key information to be collected includes the following:

Infrastructure

- type, size, and position of premise and building(s), including the number and type of building(s);
- availability and condition of:
  › water supply, connections and installation (e.g., where does the water come from?, what is the quality?, etc);
  › power supply, electrical connections and installations (e.g., is an emergency generator available?);
  › waste disposal system (e.g., how is waste handled, segregated, and disposed of?).

Medical equipment[1]

- type and number of equipment
- brand name
- model
- year of manufacture
- date of installation
- location (medical department)
- physical condition (in operation/out of order/repairable)
- spare parts required/available for repair
- tools available for inspection, maintenance, and repair
- medical equipment history if available (operation/use time, maintenance/ repair).

Health technology management

- Type of existing management structure, including responsibilities.
- Existing policy (if available).

---

1 Most of this data is collected in an inventory. Please refer to *Introduction to medical equipment inventory management* in this technical series for more details on developing an inventory.

Specific tools[2] can further assist in the collection of the appropriate information for this and other steps in the process, including:

- *Introduction to medical equipment inventory management.* Geneva, World Health Organization, 2011.
- *Computerized maintenance management system.* Geneva, World Health Organization, 2011.
- *Integrated Healthcare Technology Package (iHTP).* World Health Organization.[3]
- *Rapid health facility assessment flow chart.* International Health Facility Assessment Network, 2007.
- *Practical steps for developing health care technology policy.* Brighton, Institute of Development Studies, 2000.
- *Development of medical device policies, strategies and action plans.* Geneva, World Health Organization, 2011.

Additionally, the following are some available tools on internationally or regionally recognized standards that are useful for comparison purposes:

- *Interagency list of essential medical devices for reproductive health.* Geneva, World Health Organization, 2008.
- *Integrated Management for Emergency and Essential Surgical Care (IMEESC) tool kit.* Geneva, World Health Organization.
- *Surgical care at the district hospital.* Geneva, World Health Organization, 2003.
- *Package of essential noncommunicable (PEN) disease interventions for primary health care in low-resource settings.* Geneva, World Health Organization, 2010.
- *Medical devices by health-care facilities* (in preparation). Geneva, World Health Organization, 2011.
- *Medical devices by clinical procedures* (in preparation). Geneva, World Health Organization, 2011.
- *Models and medical equipment guidelines.* Mexico City, Centro Nacional de Excelencia Tecnológica en Salud (CENETEC).
- *Primary health care centres and first referral level hospitals. Planning guide: Equipment and renewable resources.* New York, United Nations Children's Fund, 2005.

---

2 Reference information for these tools can be found under *Useful Resources.*
3 Tool requires technical support from WHO before use.

4.4 Step IV: Baseline information on human resources

Table 5. Baseline information on human resources

Human resources	Considerations	Result
Qualification and number of human resources required to cover the required health-care demand (as defined by results of Step I)	• Availability, capacity, and capability of current human resources	• Human resource data information (staffing plan) • Education and training map

The minimum information that should be available for collection and assessment is:

- existing posts and job descriptions
- number of vacant posts
- status and availability of:
  › basic, higher or vocational education
  › continuous training
  › on-the-job training
  › human resources planning.

Further details on Step IV are not provided here, as this is outside the scope of this document and the responsibility of the GIHT. This information should be available at the HR department of your administration.

4.5 Step V: Baseline information on finances

Table 6. Baseline information on finances

Financial situation	Considerations	Result
Capacity to finance overall facility operations, including health services, health technology, and infrastructure (Steps II and III above).	• Financial resources	• Budget

The minimum information that should be available for collection and assessment is:

- budget and expenses from previous periods
- current budget
- system of monitoring/controlling budget.

Further details on Step V are not provided here, as this is outside the scope of this document and the responsibility of the GIHT. This information should be available at the financial department of your administration.

4.6   Step VI: Analysis and interpretation

Once all the information is gathered, it is possible to analyse, interpret and draw conclusions. The analysis and interpretation should be based directly on the information gathered in the manner outlined in previous steps. Therefore, keep in mind that the use of poor methodology in the information-gathering stages will undermine the ability to develop valid interpretations of the situation. In the end, this will affect the quality of the conclusions and resulting recommendations targeting the needs of the population.

Specifically for analysing medical device needs, it is necessary to compare the current inventory list (results of Step III above) with an internationally- or regionally-recognized standard for the type of facility and/or intervention being reviewed, and assess the respective gap. Using spreadsheets in a programme such as Excel can be helpful, but if there is a large amount of data to compare, it may be best to use the inventory section of a CMMS, if available, for such purposes.

The recent WHO background paper entitled: *A stepwise approach to identify gaps in medical devices (availability matrix and survey methodology)*, is a result of the Priority Medical Devices project, and it might be a helpful tool during this stage of the process.

4.7   Step VII: Prioritization and appraisal of options

After having analysed the information gathered in the earlier steps of the needs assessment process, and having drawn conclusions, there should now be a reasonably clear picture of the needs of the target population. Decisions regarding the actions to take will depend on several crucial and closely connected activities. These include:

- **Prioritization:** If there are insufficient resources to meet all the identified needs, it may be necessary to rank them in order to decide which needs should be met first and which will be met later.
- **Option appraisal:** There may be more than one way of meeting the needs identified. Various options should be considered, and the evidence in favour of each should be weighed carefully.

- **Implementation:** When agreement has been reached about how the needs are to be met, an action plan and timetable should be drawn up, including a plan for resource allocation.

In practice, the tasks of prioritization and option appraisal are directly linked. Both must be considered together.

4.7.1   Prioritization
When sufficient resources are not available to meet all the identified needs (which is the case in most circumstances), it is important for prioritization to occur. Prioritization is a strategic process, undertaken by those responsible for the commissioning of services. Those involved in prioritizing should also consider the opinions of service users and service providers regarding how to

prioritize needs. However, they may not always agree, so priority is best given to those areas where they do.

The way in which decisions are made with regard to identified priorities will depend on local circumstances. National priorities and the availability of required resources are often what prompts the needs assessment process. Therefore, the purpose of this step is to determine specifically what should be done, how, and in what order. For example, national and local policy may require that services should be provided for maternal and child health. In this case, the local needs assessment will focus on identifying the specific needs of women/mothers and newborns in the local area, their prioritization, and what is particularly required (in terms of medical devices) in order to render the required services that will allow these priorities to be realized.

4.7.2 Option appraisal
In most cases, there will be more than one way of responding to the needs which have been identified. The options you choose will depend on several factors, including:

- how the needs are prioritized
- what the likely impact of each option will be
- the availability of resources.

Table 7 provides one way of thinking about the options for change following a needs assessment.

Table 7. Plan, Do, Study, Act (PDSA) prioritization matrix

Finances/resources required to implement change	Likely impact of change	
	Low	High
Low	Soft target: Wait	Win: Go!
High	Refrain or Wait	Challenging: Wait

The aim will be to give first priority to actions that will have the highest positive impact on the ability to provide optimal services to the target population, as well as require the fewest additional resources.

At the other extreme, it is better to avoid making changes that are likely to have a low impact but which require a high level of resources. In between are those actions that are likely to have a high impact, but will also demand high resources. In most circumstances, these would not be selected for immediate action either, but rather, considered as long-term options.

Similarly, so called 'soft targets' are those actions requiring few resources but having little impact. It may be tempting/attractive to go ahead with these actions, but they can prove to be a distraction from the more high-impact actions. For this reason, it is usually better to wait until the 'quick wins' have been successfully implemented first.

Hooper and Longworth (2002) suggest that a number of key questions should be addressed when appraising the options and prioritizing the needs following a needs assessment exercise. These questions focus on the issues of impact, changeability, acceptability and resource feasibility, and are adapted here for the application of needs assessment of health technology.

Table 8. Key questions for prioritizing and appraisal of options

Key questions to ask when appraising the options and prioritizing
Impact   • Which changes would have the greatest positive impact in meeting needs?   • Do the identified needs relate to a local or a national priority (e.g., maternal and child health, HIV/AIDS, etc.)?   • What would be the implications of not addressing the needs?
Changeability   • Which things can be changed and effectively improved?   • What evidence is there of effective interventions?   • Can negative impacts be stopped or reduced?   • Are there national or local, professional or organizational policies that set out guidelines on what should be done (e.g., national frameworks, national guidance, etc.)?
Acceptability   • Which of the options for change are likely to be most acceptable to the health service providers, to the target population, and to the managers?   • What might be the 'knock-on' effects, or unintended consequences, of making a change?
Resource feasibility   • Which resources are required to implement the proposed changes?   • Can existing resources be used differently?   • Which resources will be released if ineffective actions are stopped/changed (e.g., proper management of health technology, etc.)?   • Are there other resources available which have not been given prior consideration (e.g., income generation of laboratory services, consideration of public-private partnerships, assistance from NGOs, etc.)?   • Which of the actions will achieve the greatest impact for the resources used?

4.7.3 Developing an implementation plan

Once priorities and the ways to address these priorities are agreed upon, the next step is to develop an action plan for implementation. An implementation plan should be **realistic, achievable** and **adequately fundable**, while at the same time able to clearly outline the various stages of the implementation process.

It is important that health service providers are included in discussions regarding the implementation plan – and are supportive of it – because at an operational level, they will be directly involved in the implementation and introduction of the agreed changes to existing services.

A good implementation plan includes:

- a statement of the aims and objectives of the planned action, and the specific steps and milestones required to achieve it;
- the names of the individuals responsible for carrying out each part of the plan, what they will do and when, and the skills and training they will need (in particular, with a focus on health technology management, policy and structure);
- details of the resources that will be required (including devices, and if applicable, administrative, managerial, and IT systems), and where they will come from;
- a clear understanding of how the plan will be kept on track, how the implementation of each component of the plan will be measured, and how the relevant people will be kept motivated and involved.

5 Concluding remarks

The needs assessment process is a powerful tool for determining medical device needs at the facility, regional and/or country level. By collecting baseline information and comparing it to a desired standard, the existing gap can be identified.

Determining how to best use the resources available to fill that gap will lead to a prioritization of activities that can eventually lead to a more efficient provision of health services and better quality of care.

6 Useful resources

All URLs accessed 30th March 2011

For these and more resources, please visit the World Health Organization Library Information System (WHOLIS) at http://dosei.who.int, or the e-Documentation centre for WHO Health Technologies/Medical devices at http://hinfo.humaninfo.ro/gsdl/ healthtechdocs.

Medical equipment maintenance programme overview. Geneva, World Health Organization, 2011.

Health technology assessment of medical devices. Geneva, World Health Organization, 2011.

Service Availability Mapping (SAM), World Health Organization (http://www.who.int/ healthinfo/systems/serviceavailabilitymapping/en).

Rapid health facility assessment flow chart. New York, International Health Facility Assessment Network, 2007 (http://ihfan.org/home/docs/attachments/ms-08-28_ flowchart.pdf).

Introduction to medical equipment inventory management. Geneva, World Health Organization, 2011.

Computerized maintenance management system. Geneva, World Health Organization, 2011.

Integrated Healthcare Technology Package (iHTP), World Health Organization (http:// www.ihtp.info).

Temple-Bird C. *Practical steps for developing health care technology policy.* Brighton, Institute of Development Studies, 2000.

Development of medical device policies, strategies and action plans. Geneva, World Health Organization, 2011.

Interagency list of essential medical devices for reproductive health. Geneva, World Health Organization, 2008 (http://whqlibdoc.who.int/hq/2008/WHO_PSM_PAR_2008.1_ eng.pdf).

Integrated Management for Emergency and Essential Surgical Care (IMEESC) tool. Geneva, World Health Organization (http://www.who.int/surgery/publications/imeesc/ en/index.html).

Surgical care at the district hospital. Geneva, World Health Organization, 2003 (http://www.who.int/surgery/publications/scdh_manual/en).

Package of essential noncommunicable (PEN) disease interventions for primary health care in low-resource settings. Geneva, World Health Organization, 2010 (http://whqlibdoc.who.int/publications/2010/9789241598996_eng.pdf).

Medical devices by health-care facilities (in preparation). Geneva, World Health Organization, 2011.

Medical devices by clinical procedures (in preparation). Geneva, World Health Organization, 2011.

Models and medical equipment guidelines. Mexico City, Centro Nacional de Excelencia Tecnológica en Salud (CENETEC) (http://www.cenetec.salud.gob.mx/interior/modelos_equip.html).

Primary health care centres and first referral level hospitals. Planning guide: Equipment and renewable resources. New York, United Nations Children's Fund, 2005 (http://www.unicef.org/supply/files/050307PlanningGuideHandbookAug2005%281%29.pdf).

A stepwise approach to identify gaps in medical devices (availability matrix and survey methodology). Background paper 1. Geneva, World Health Organization, 2010 (http://whqlibdoc.who.int/hq/2010/WHO_HSS_EHT_DIM_10.1_eng.pdf).

Priority medical devices project. World Health Organization (http://www.who.int/medical_devices/access/en/index.html).

Hooper J and Longworth P. (2002). *Health needs assessment workbook.* Health Development Agency, 2002 (http://www.nice.org.uk/niceMedia/documents/hna.pdf).

Certificado de Necesidad (Certificate of Need). Mexico City, Centro Nacional de Excelencia Tecnológica en Salud (CENETEC) (http://www.cenetec.salud.gob.mx/interior/cert_nec.html).

'How to Manage' series of health care technology guides. St Albans, Ziken International (Health Partners International), 2005 (http://www.healthpartners-int.co.uk/our_expertise/how_to_manage_series.html).

Liu, X. *Policy tools for allocative efficiency of health services.* Geneva, World Health Organization, 2003 (http://whqlibdoc.who.int/publications/2003/9241562528.pdf).

Appendix A
Certificate of need process

The Certificate of Need is a planning tool used to support decision-makers in evaluating investments of highly-specialized and expensive medical equipment, based on technical, epidemiological, and cost-benefit criteria in order to best optimize resources.[1] Many countries do not have this process in place but may be something decision-makers may want to consider. For those countries who have or will implement this process, it is important to take into consideration the following when applying for a certificate of need.

- General Data
  - › Place
  - › Catchment area
  - › Epidemiology information
  - › Mortality/morbidity
  - › Applicants data.

- Description of need
  - › Service characteristics
  - › Clinical procedures required
  - › Number of referred patients to another site
  - › Other available equipment in the area.

- Proposal
  - › Medical equipment
  - › Staff
  - › Infrastructure.

- Resources needed
  - › Investment
  - › Operational costs
  - › Sources of financing.

---

1 CENETEC definition translated from Spanish (http://www.cenetec.salud.gob.mx/interior/cert_nec.html)

The flow chart below demonstrates the process for obtaining a certificate of need.

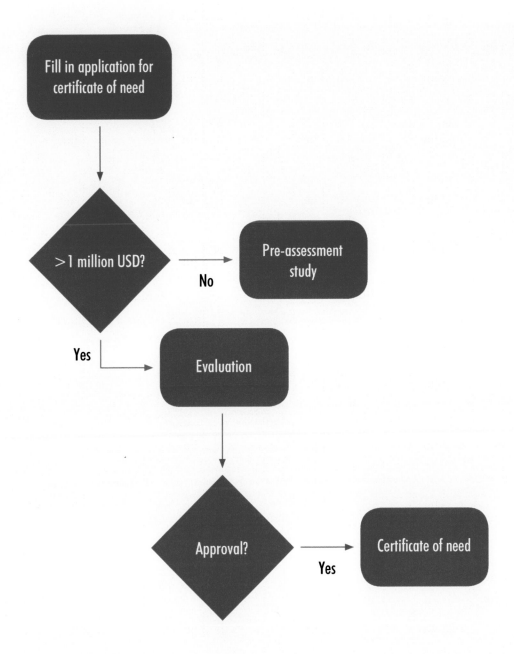

THIS BOOK BELONGS TO...

Name: Age:

Favourite player:

2022/23

My Predictions...   Actual...

The Canaries' final position:

The Canaries' top scorer:

Championship winners:

Championship top scorer:

FA Cup winners:

EFL Cup winners:

Contributors: Peter Rogers

A TWOCAN PUBLICATION

ISBN: 978-1-914588-68-6 £10

CONTENTS

When it came to choosing Norwich City's Goal of the Season for 2021/22, there really was only ever one show in Town or in this case Toon - Teemu Pukki's magnificent left-footed volley that secured a point in the Canaries' 1-1 draw away to Newcastle United in November 2021.

City made the long haul to St James' Park for a televised midweek match against a Newcastle side who were propping up the Premier League table. Norwich clearly arrived on Tyneside full of confidence having picked up seven points from their previous three Premier League fixtures and had been given a fresh boost of self belief by new head coach Dean Smith.

The match took a big swing in Norwich's favour when home defender Ciaran Clark was shown a ninth-minute red card for a professional foul on Pukki. However, the ten men of Newcastle rallied and took a 61st-minute lead when Callum Wilson converted a highly-controversial penalty. The spot-kick was awarded by the video assistant referee after Billy Gilmour had been adjudged to have blocked Federico Fernández's header with his arm.

Despite falling behind against the run of play, Norwich continued to look the better of the two sides and justifiably salvaged a point eleven minutes from time when Pukki struck his stunning equaliser. The goal silenced St James' Park and came after Martin Dúbravka's weak punch sent Gilmour's cross into the path of Dimitris Giannoulis and he teed up Pukki for a memorable finish in front of the travelling Yellow Army behind the goal.

The goal was Pukki's fifth of an eleven-goal campaign as the Finnish international hit double figures for the fourth consecutive season since arriving at Carrow Road in the summer of 2018.

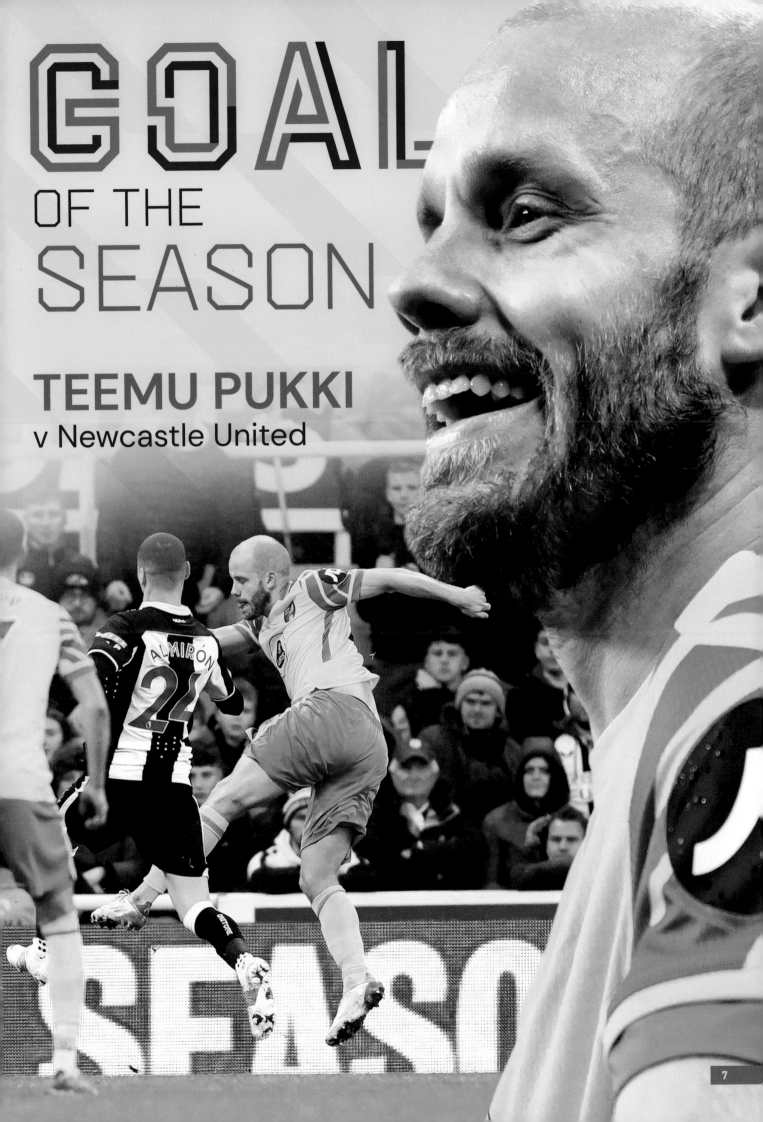

GOAL
OF THE
SEASON

TEEMU PUKKI
v Newcastle United

NUMBER OF SEASONS WITH THE CANARIES:

10

NORWICH CITY APPEARANCES:

352

NORWICH CITY GOALS:

54

PLAYER OF THE SEASON:

2017/18

LEGEND

WES HOOLAHAN

NORWICH CITY ACHIEVEMENTS:

League One champions 2009/10. Championship runners-up 2010/11. Championship Play-Off winners 2014/15.

MAJOR STRENGTH:

Defence splitting passes.

INTERNATIONAL ACTION:

Wes won full caps for the Republic of Ireland and played in Euro 2016 while a City player.

FINEST HOUR:

Wes kept his cool to fire home a penalty in front of the Barclay End to open the scoring the 2014/15 Play-Off semi-final victory over Ipswich Town.

Wes Hoolahan and Emi Buendía are two players small in stature that both made a big impression during their respective Norwich City careers.

Both players fall into the tiny terrors category and both have hero status here at Carrow Road. Clear match-winners on their day who are blessed with the ability to score goals and create chances for teammates, these two former Canaries had pure skill in abundance.

But who was the best? That's for you to decide and here are a few facts and figures from their time in yellow and green to help you reach your conclusion...

It's a tough call!

NUMBER OF SEASONS WITH THE CANARIES:

3

NORWICH CITY APPEARANCES:

121

NORWICH CITY GOALS:

24

PLAYER OF THE SEASON:

2020/21

LEGEND

EMI BUENDÍA

NORWICH CITY ACHIEVEMENTS:

Championship champions 2018/19.
Championship champions 2020/21.

MAJOR STRENGTH:

Immaculate close control and dribbling ability.

INTERNATIONAL ACTION:

Called into the Argentina squad while still a Norwich player, his international debut did not arrive until after he left City.

FINEST HOUR:

Emi struck the vital goal to beat promotion rivals Brentford 1–0 at Carrow Road in March 2021.

TODD
CANTWELL

14

Close control in tight situations creates havoc in opposition defences – particularly when receiving the ball in the air – and nine times out of ten, when a striker receives the ball, he has his back to goal.

SOCCER SKILLS

RECEIVING THE BALL

Quite often the ball will arrive in the air, and good strikers have to be able to cope with that – controlling and turning in one movement, ready for the instant shot.

EXERCISE 1

In an area 20m x 10m, two players A and A2 test the man in the middle, B, by initially throwing the ball at him in the air, with the instruction to turn and play in to the end man – if possible using only two touches.

The middle player is changed regularly, and to make things more realistic, the end players progress to chipping the ball into the middle. The middle player is asked to receive and turn using chest, thigh, or instep.

KEY FACTORS

1 Assess flight early – get in position.
2 Cushion the ball.
3 Be half turned as you receive.

EXERCISE 2

A progression of this exercise is the following, where the ball is chipped or driven in to the striker from varying positions. He has to receive with his back to goal, and using just two touches in total if possible, shoot past the keeper into the goal!

To make this even more difficult, a defender can be brought in eventually. For younger children, the 'servers' should throw the ball to ensure consistent quality.

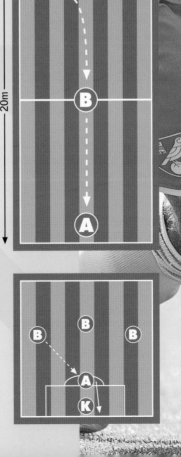

11

CHAMPIONSHIP 2022/23 SQUAD

1 TIM **KRUL**

Goalkeeper **DOB:** 03/04/1988 **COUNTRY:** Netherlands

Norwich City's first choice goalkeeper since joining the club in 2018, Tim Krul has twice been a Championship title-winner during his Carrow Road career.

The penalty saving hero of City's memorable FA Cup fifth-round victory at the Tottenham Hotspur Stadium in March 2020 - Krul is a full Dutch international and the most experienced member of the Canaries' squad.

2 MAX **AARONS**

Defender **DOB:** 04/01/2000 **COUNTRY:** England

One of the best defenders to emerge from the Norwich City Academy, 22-year-old attacking right-back Max Aarons already has two Championship title-winners' medals to his name despite his tender years.

Ever since scoring in only his second game for the club, in an EFL Cup tie away to Cardiff City in August 2018, Aarons has made the City right-back berth his own with over 150 league appearances in yellow and green. .

3 SAM **BYRAM**

Defender DOB: **16/09/1993** COUNTRY: **England**

Sam Byram was recruited from West Ham United ahead of Norwich City's 2019/20 Premier League campaign.

A versatile defender whose natural position is at right-back, Byram can also fill in at left-back and in 2021/22 even operated in a central defensive role. Injuries have hampered the 29-year-old's time with Norwich and both player and club will be hopeful he can play a big part in City's 2022/23 Championship campaign.

4 ANDREW **OMOBAMIDELE**

Defender DOB: **23/06/2002** COUNTRY: **Republic of Ireland**

Giant central defender Andrew Omobamidele is another player that has progressed through the Norwich City Academy to make his mark at Carrow Road.

Such was Omobamidele's impressive form when breaking through to the first team, that his talent was quickly spotted by his country and he won his first full international cap for the Republic of Ireland in September 2021. Calm in possession and with great awareness of danger, Omobamidele looks all set to have a great career ahead of him.

5 GRANT **HANLEY**

Defender DOB: **20/11/1991** COUNTRY: **Scotland**

Scotland international defender and Norwich City captain, Grant Hanley is the rock at the heart of the Norwich City defence.

Signed from Newcastle United in August 2017, Hanley had previously made his name with Blackburn Rovers. Skipper of two Norwich City Championship title-winning campaigns, the Scot has now made over 150 appearances in the Norwich City first team and is one of the first names on head coach Dean's Smith's team sheet.

6 BEN **GIBSON**

Defender DOB: **15/01/1993** COUNTRY: **England**

Born in the midst of Norwich City's greatest Premier League campaign of 1992/93 – central defender Ben Gibson was perhaps destined to play for the Canaries.

A former England under-21 star while at Middlesbrough, Gibson joined the Canaries following a difficult time with Burnley. After signing for Norwich in the summer of 2020 he ended his debut campaign in Norfolk as a Championship title winner.

7 MILOT **RASHICA**

Midfielder DOB: 28/06/1996 COUNTRY: Kosovo

Attacking wide midfielder Milot Rashica joined the Canaries from Werder Bremen in June 2021.

Blessed with great close control and a fierce shot, the 26-year-old has the ability to excite supporters while causing major problems for opposing defenders. A full Kosovo international with over 40 appearances and eight international goals to his name, Rashica agreed a four-year deal at Carrow Road.

8 ISAAC **HAYDEN**

Midfielder DOB: 22/03/1995 COUNTRY: **England**

A powerful central midfield presence that can affect games at both ends of the pitch, Isaac Hayden became Dean Smith's first Norwich City signing when he agreed a season-long loan at Carrow Road in the summer of 2022.

On loan from Newcastle United with a view to a potential permanent transfer, Hayden was sidelined in the opening weeks of the season, but is someone who will have a major role to play as the 2022/23 campaign unfolds.

15 SAM McCALLUM

Defender **DOB:** 02/09/2000 **COUNTRY:** England

Signed from Coventry City, attacking left-back Sam McCallum has been loaned back to the Sky Blues and has also spent a period on loan in the Championship with Queens Park Rangers.

Having impressed in pre-season, the 2022/23 campaign appeared to be his breakthrough season with the Canaries. Sadly an injury sustained in the EFL Cup match with Birmingham City in August will see him out of action until after the mid-season break for the 2022 FIFA World Cup finals in Qatar.

17 GABRIEL SARA

Midfielder **DOB:** 26/06/1999 **COUNTRY:** Brazil

Arriving from Brazil in July 2022, midfielder Gabriel Sara should certainly be at home in green and yellow!

The 23-year-old Brazilian was signed from Sao Paulo and made his Canary debut in the opening home game of the season as City drew 1-1 at home to Wigan Athletic. A real box-to-box bundle of energy, his signing has certainly excited the Carrow Road faithful.

19   JACOB **SØRENSEN**

Midfielder   DOB: **03/03/1998**   COUNTRY: **Denmark**

A popular and extremely versatile member of the City squad, defensive midfielder Jacob Sørensen joined the club in July 2020 from Esbjerg fB.

With the ability to operate in defensive roles as well as his preferred central-midfield slot, Sørensen's adaptability has seen him feature regularly for both Daniel Farke and Dean Smith in recent times. The Dane netted a stunning goal in the EFL Cup victory over Birmingham City at Carrow Road in August 2022.

20   AARON **RAMSEY**

Midfielder   DOB: **21/01/2003**   COUNTRY: **England**

Attacking midfielder Aaron Ramsey joined the Canaries on a season-long loan from Aston Villa.

The England under-19 international's talents are well known to City head coach Dean Smith and his assistant Craig Shakespeare who both worked with Ramsey at Villa. With the ability to operate off either flank, the teenager offers Norwich City great options in wide areas.

21 DANEL **SINANI**

Midfielder DOB: **05/04/1997** COUNTRY: **Luxembourg**

After impressing at Championship level while on loan at Huddersfield Town last season, Luxembourg international striker Danel Sinani made a positive start to the current season with the Canaries.

On target in the EFL Cup victory over Birmingham City, Sinani then netted his first league goal for City as they defeated his Terriers' teammates from last season 2–1 at Carrow Road.

22 TEEMU **PUKKI**

Forward DOB: **29/03/1990** COUNTRY: **Finland**

Voted Norwich City's player of the season for a second time in 2021/22, Finnish ace Teemu Pukki was once again top scorer at Carrow Road for a fourth consecutive season.

A real penalty box poacher, Pukki remains the go to man for goals for both club and country. With 78 Norwich City career goals to his name as at the start of 2022/23, the Canary fans will be hoping to see him reach the century mark this season.

CHAMPIONSHIP 2022/23 SQUAD

23 **KENNY McLEAN**

Midfielder DOB: 08/01/1992 COUNTRY: Scotland

A full Scotland international, midfield maestro Kenny McLean is now in his fifth season with the Canaries having joined from Aberdeen in 2018.

A consistent performer throughout his Norwich City career, McLean has two Championship title-winning medals to his name. Just like fellow countryman Grant Hanley, McLean has now amassed over 150 appearances in a Norwich City shirt.

24 **JOSH SARGENT**

Forward DOB: 20/02/2000 COUNTRY: USA

American international forward Josh Sargent suffered a difficult first season at Carrow Road as Norwich City battled to avoid relegation from the Premier League.

However, the hard working front man has made an impressive start to the 2022/23 season with four goals in August as City recorded victories over Huddersfield Town, Millwall and Sunderland. Those goals have given Sargent a real confidence boost and he appears all set to play a pivotal role for Dean Smith's team this season.

25 ONEL **HERNÁNDEZ**

Midfielder DOB: **01/02/1993** COUNTRY: **Cuba**

A real crowd favourite at Carrow Road, flying winger Onel Hernández is a Cuban international who has the ability to thrill supporters with his direct running and attacking approach to games.

Another player to have featured in both of Norwich's recent Championship title successes, the 29-year-old spent last season on loan at Middlesbrough and Birmingham City, but now looks to make up for lost time upon his return to his spiritual home in Norfolk.

26 MARCELINO **NÚÑEZ**

Midfielder DOB: **01/03/2000** COUNTRY: **Chile**

A real creative force in the heart of the Norwich City midfield, Canary fans have been highly impressed with what they have seen from Marcelino Núñez following his summer 2022 signing from Universidad Catolica.

Only 22-years-old, Núñez has already made ten international appearances for his country and has swiftly adapted to the English game. He netted his first goal for Norwich with a curling free-kick against Hull City.

27 JONATHAN **ROWE**

Midfielder   DOB: **30/04/2003**   COUNTRY: **England**

A tricky attacking midfielder with quick feet and an eye for goal, Jonathan Rowe is another youngster to emerge from the club's Academy.

Rowe was handed his first-team debut by head coach Dean Smith in a Premier League fixture at Crystal Palace in December 2021. He went on to make 15 first-team appearances in total last season – all of them from the substitute's bench.

28 ANGUS **GUNN**

Goalkeeper   DOB: **22/01/1996**   COUNTRY: **England**

Angus Gunn is now in his third spell with Norwich City. Having been an Academy player before returning to Carrow Road in 2017/18 with a season-long loan from Manchester City, Gunn then joined the club permanently in 2021 from Southampton.

The son of Canary legend Bryan, Angus is an exceptional talent who is expected to push Tim Krul all the way for the goalkeeper's position at Carrow Road this season.

TRUE OR FALSE

Here are ten fun footy True or False teasers for you to tackle!

2. The FIFA World Cup in 2026 is due to be hosted in the USA, Mexico and Canada

3. Manchester City's former ground was called Maine Park

1. England star Harry Kane has only ever played club football for Tottenham Hotspur

4. Liverpool's Jürgen Klopp has never managed the German national team

5. Gareth Southgate succeeded Roy Hodgson as England manager

6. Manchester United's Old Trafford has the largest capacity in the Premier League

7. Jordan Pickford began his football career at Everton

8. Huddersfield Town's nickname is the Terriers

9. Norwich City signed Grant Hanley from Newcastle

10. Teemu Pukki's last Premier League goal for the Canaries was a penalty

26

MAX
AARONS

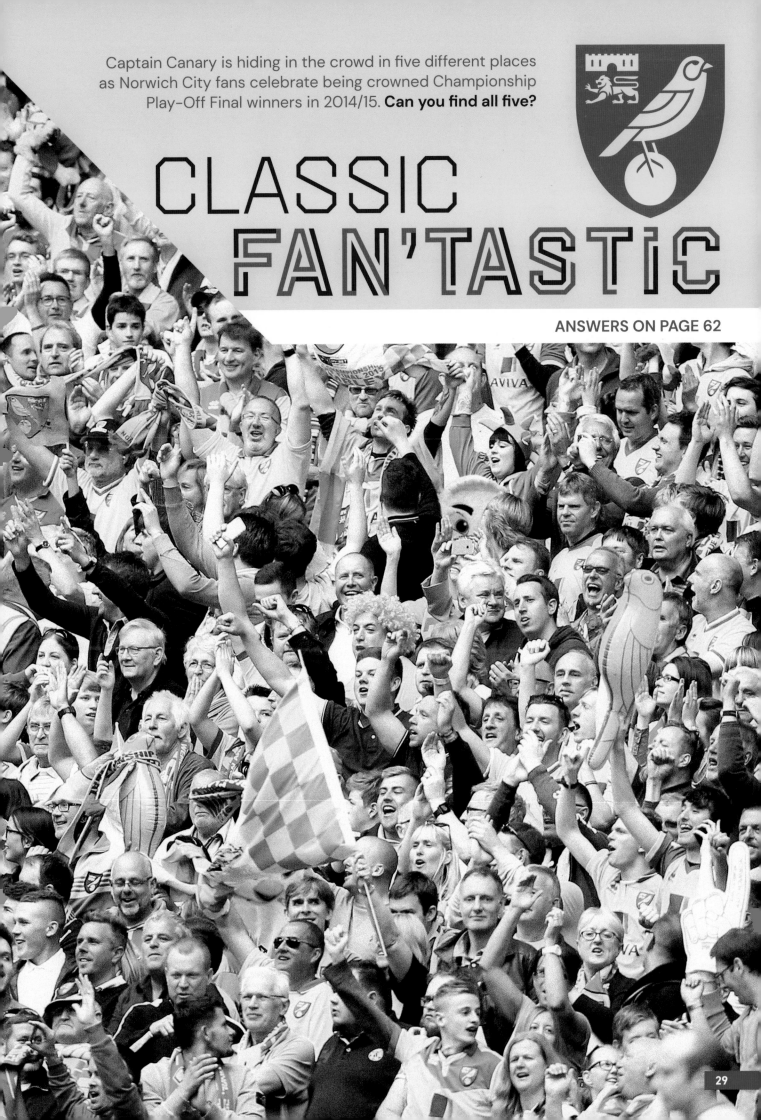

Captain Canary is hiding in the crowd in five different places as Norwich City fans celebrate being crowned Championship Play-Off Final winners in 2014/15. **Can you find all five?**

CLASSIC
FAN'TASTIC

ANSWERS ON PAGE 62

29

TEEMU
PUKKI

22

Defending is not just about stopping the attackers and clearing your lines. Making the best of possession you have just won is vital – although the danger has to be cleared, it is important for your team to keep hold of the ball.

SOCCER SKILLS

LONG PASSES

When passing your way out of defence, and short, side–foot passes are not possible, the longer pass, driven over the heads of midfield players, can be used.

EXERCISE

In an area 40m x 10m, A1 and A2 try to pass accurately to each other, with a defender B, in the middle between them. Player B must attempt to stop the pass if possible, and A1 and A2, must keep the ball within the area of the grids.

After each successful long pass, the end player will exchange a shorter pass with B before passing long again, thus keeping the exercise realistic and also keeping the defender in the middle involved. The player in the middle should be changed every few minutes, and a 'count' of successful passes made for each player.

KEY FACTORS

1 Approach at an angle.
2 Non kicking foot placed next to the ball.
3 Eye on the ball.
4 Strike underneath the ball & follow through.

Practice is the key to striking a consistently accurate long pass and to developing the timing and power required.

The same end result could be achieved by bending the pass around the defender instead of over him, and this pass could be practised in the same exercise, by striking the football on its outer edge (instead of underneath) which will impart the spin required to make the ball 'bend' around the defender - not an easy skill!

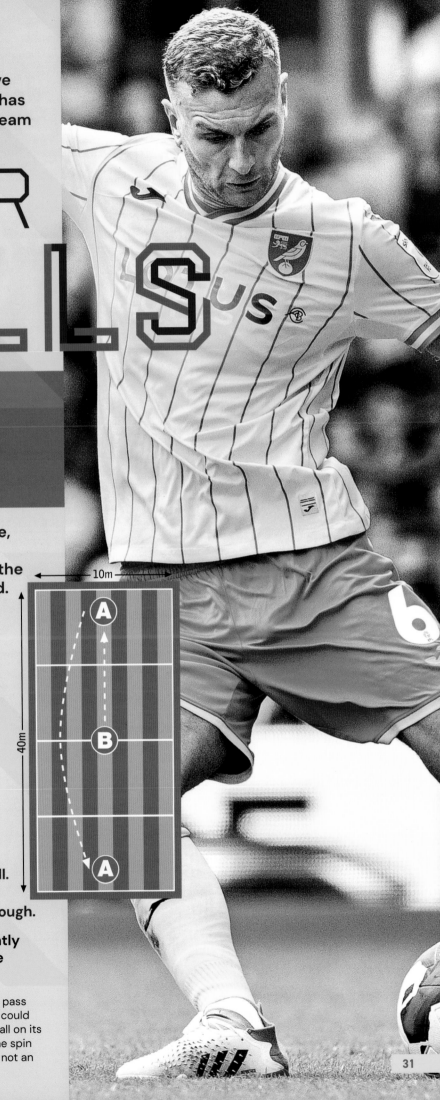

10m

40m

A

B

A

PLAYER
OF THE
SEASON

TEEMU PUKKI

The conclusion of the 2021/22 season saw City's Finnish international striker Teemu Pukki presented with the Barry Butler Memorial Trophy for the second time in his Carrow Road career after supporters voted him their Norwich City Player of the Season once again.

Having won the award back in 2018/19 when he scored an incredible 29 league goals in City's Championship title-winning campaign, Pukki was leading scorer again in 2021/22 netting eleven Premier League goals as Norwich attempted to avoid relegation.

After scoring against Leicester City and Watford, Pukki's third goal of the season coincided with the Canaries' first Premier League win of the campaign as Norwich won 2-1 away against fellow promoted side Brentford. Pukki also took the mantle of scoring the first goal of new manager Dean Smith's reign as City got a new era off to a winning start with a 2-1 Carrow Road triumph over Southampton.

The pick of Pukki's eleven goals last season was certainly his stunning strike in the 1-1 draw away to Newcastle United at the end of November as the ace marksman took his tally to three goals in four games in what was a real purple patch for the 32-year-old crowd favourite.

In mid-April and with supporters beginning to think about voting for their Player of the Season, Pukki scored in the 2-0 home victory over Burnley and then in the narrow 3-2 defeat away to Manchester United.

Once the yellow army had cast their votes, Pukki topped the poll with skipper Grant Hanley coming second and on-loan Manchester United full-back Brandon Williams third.

Pukki's goals last season took his Canary career total to 78 and saw him sit level with Grant Holt as the joint sixth highest goalscorer in the club's history.

With 55 second tier goals across his previous two seasons at Championship level, there is a real expectation that Pukki could possibly reach a century of career goals in Canary colours during the 2022/23 campaign. Should that be the case then few would bet again the finisher supreme securing a hat-trick of Player of the Season awards come the end of the current campaign.

DREAM TEAM

Pick your ultimate Norwich City dream team and design them a kit!

GABRIEL
SARA

BIRMINGHAM CITY

PRZEMYSLAW PLACHETA

A Polish international and true speed merchant, Przemyslaw Placheta is on a season long loan at St Andrew's from Championship rivals Norwich City.

The 24-year-old forward tends to operate on the left side of the Blues' attack and marked his home debut for Birmingham City with a goal in their 2-1 victory over Huddersfield Town in August.

BRISTOL CITY

ANDREAS WEIMANN

Austrian international forward Andreas Weimann was the Robins' leading scorer last season with 22 goals in 45 Championship games.

An experienced and proven goalscorer at this level, Weimann, who had scored goals at second tier level for Watford, Derby County and Wolves before moving to Ashton Gate, netted in each of the first three league games of the new 2022/23 season.

BLACKBURN ROVERS

LEWIS TRAVIS

All-action central midfielder Lewis Travis was at the heart of Blackburn Rovers' impressive 2021/22 Championship campaign featuring in all bar one of the club's league games last season.

With the ability to carry the ball forward and help his team turn defence into attack, 25-year-old Travis has won many admirers for his energetic displays in the Rovers engine room.

BURNLEY

JAY RODRIGUEZ

Now in his second spell at Turf Moor, Burnley-born forward Jay Rodriguez is expected to have a big role to play for the Clarets in 2022/23 as the club looks to bounce back to the Premier League at the first attempt.

A former England international, Rodriguez played top-flight football for Southampton and WBA before rejoining the Clarets in 2019.

BLACKPOOL

THEO CORBEANU

Blackpool signed Canadian international forward Theo Corbeanu on a season-long loan from Wolves in July 2022.

Standing at 6ft 3ins, the 20-year-old brings a real presence to the Seasiders' attack and was on target in both of Blackpool's thrilling 3-3 draws against Burnley and Bristol City in August and following the sale of Josh Bowler he could well be the go-to man for goals at Bloomfield Road in 2022/23.

CARDIFF CITY

MAX WATTERS

Exciting striker Max Watters will be looking to cement his place in the Cardiff City attack in 2022/23. After joining the Bluebirds in January 2021 from Crawley, Watters was loaned to League One MK Dons in 2021/22.

However, Cardiff boss Steve Morison has handed Max the chance to make his mark with a series of starts as Cardiff's got the new season underway in impressive form.

COVENTRY CITY
CALLUM O'HARE

Attacking midfielder Callum O'Hare enjoyed a highly impressive 2021/22 season and has gained the reputation of being both City's star performer and one of the most creative midfielders operating in the Championship.

With fantastic close control and superb awareness of teammates, O'Hare is blessed with great balance when in possession and the eye for a decisive pass.

LUTON TOWN
ELIJAH ADEBAYO

Elijah Adebayo topped the Luton Town scoring charts last season with 16 Championship goals at the Hatters reached the end-of-season Play-Offs.

A strong target man, Adebayo is expected to form an impressive strike partnership at Kenilworth Road this season with Luton new boy Carlton Morris who joined in the summer from Barnsley.

HUDDERSFIELD TOWN
JORDAN RHODES

Striker Jordan Rhodes has netted over 200 career goals since emerging though the Ipswich Town youth system back in 2007.

Now in his second spell with Huddersfield Town, 32-year-old Rhodes scored 87 goals in 148 outings during his first spell at the club. He returned to the Terriers in 2021 and scored the winning goal in last season's Play-Off semi-final against Luton Town.

MIDDLESBROUGH
MATT CROOKS

An all-action attacking midfielder who can also operate as an out-and-out striker, Matt Crooks joined Middlesbrough in the summer of 2021.

Signed on the back of a number of impressive seasons with Rotherham United, Crooks hit double figures in his first season at the Riverside and is sure to play a big part for Chris Wilder's team this time around.

HULL CITY
ÓSCAR ESTUPIÑÁN

The Tigers completed the signing of Columbian international striker Oscar Estupinan in July 2022.

His arrival created a level of excitement around the MKM Stadium and the Columbian soon showed his capabilities with both goals as Hull pulled off a surprise victory over Norwich City in August 2022. A strong and mobile front man, Estupiñán's goals may well help fire the Tigers up the table this season.

MILLWALL
BARTOSZ BIALKOWSKI

Polish international keeper Bartosz Bialkowski has been ever present in the Lions' last two Championship campaigns.

The 6ft 4in stopper is widely regarded as one of the most reliable goalkeepers in the division. Blessed with excellent reflexes, Bialkowski is an intimidating opponent in one-on-one situations and his command of the penalty area certainly provides great confidence for those operating in front of him

MULTIPLE CHOICE

Here are ten Multiple Choice questions to challenge your footy knowledge!

GOOD LUCK...

ANSWERS ON PAGE 62

1. What was the name of Tottenham Hotspur's former ground?

A) White Rose Park
B) White Foot Way
C) White Hart Lane

2. Which club did Steven Gerrard leave to become Aston Villa manager?

A) Liverpool,
B) Glasgow Rangers
C) LA Galaxy

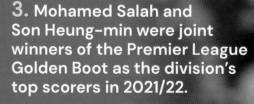

3. Mohamed Salah and Son Heung-min were joint winners of the Premier League Golden Boot as the division's top scorers in 2021/22.

How many goals did they score?
A) 23   B) 24   C) 25

4. What is the nationality of Manchester United boss Erik ten Hag?

A) Swiss   B) Dutch
C) Swedish

5. Where do Everton play their home games?

A) Goodison Road
B) Goodison Way
C) Goodison Park

6. From which club did Arsenal sign goalkeeper Aaron Ramsdale?

A) Sheffield United
B) Stoke City
C) AFC Bournemouth

7. What is Raheem Sterling's middle name?

A) Shaun
B) Shaquille
C) Silver

8. Who won the 2021/22 League One Play-Off final?

A) Wigan Athletic
B) Sunderland
C) Rotherham United

9. How many times have Norwich City won at Wembley Stadium?
A) Once, B) Twice
C) Three times

10. From which club did the Canaries sign Angus Gunn?

A) Manchester City,
B) Leicester City
C) Southampton

JOSH SARGENT

24

NUMBER OF SEASONS WITH THE CANARIES:

7

NORWICH CITY APPEARANCES:

306

NORWICH CITY GOALS:

96

PLAYER OF THE SEASON:

1998/99
1999/00

LEGEND

IWAN ROBERTS

Strikers Iwan Roberts and Grant Holt both won the adulation of the Carrow Road faithful as consistent goalscorers for Norwich City.

Two powerful front-men who led the City attack and embraced the responsibility of being Norwich's go-to men for goals throughout their Canary careers. Both players possessed great physical presence and ensured that any central defender who was challenged with the task of marking them would certainly have known they had been in a game.

Each player boasted an impressive goals-to-games ratio but who was the best? Well that's for you to decide and here are a selection of facts and figures from their time with Norwich City to help you make your choice...

Once again, it's a tough call!

NORWICH CITY ACHIEVEMENTS:

Nationwide First Division Play-Off finalists 2001/02.
Nationwide Division One winners 2003/04.

MAJOR STRENGTH:

Superb winner of balls in the air.

INTERNATIONAL ACTION:

Iwan won eight of his 15 full caps for Wales a Norwich City player.

FINEST HOUR:

Iwan delighted the huge travelling Canary contingent inside Cardiff's Millennium Stadium when he opened the scoring the 2001/02 Play-Off final match against Birmingham City.

LEGEND

GRANT HOLT

NUMBER OF SEASONS WITH THE CANARIES:
4

NORWICH CITY APPEARANCES:
168

NORWICH CITY GOALS:
78

PLAYER OF THE SEASON:
2009/10, 2010/11 & 2011/12

NORWICH CITY ACHIEVEMENTS:
League One champions 2009/10.
Championship runners-up (2010/11).

MAJOR STRENGTH:
A real penalty box predator both in the air and on the ground.

INTERNATIONAL ACTION:
To the dismay of the Norwich fans, Holt was never capped by England despite his impressive Premier League form in 2011/12.

FINEST HOUR:
A never-to-be-forgotten hat-trick in the 4-1 drubbing of East Anglian rivals Ipswich Town in November 2010.

45

EVERY TEAM OF THE CHAMPIONSHIP IS
HIDDEN IN THE GRID, EXCEPT FOR ONE.
...CAN YOU WORK OUT WHICH ONE?

CLUB SEARCH

```
J B R A L G V N O R W I C H C I T Y M H
A I M O U Z E K F X R W F U C C D I S W
B R I S T O L C I T Y C B L A E S W P E
L M D A O H V E L P D N A L R E D N U S
A I D C N B E L W L O Q I C D W Y R L T
C N L I T U D R E I A V A I I Q P D O B
K G E T O U N U H P U W H T F I T E L R
B H S E W H E B N A I O L Y F M U T S O
U A B L N Y H T V R M J N L C H D I C M
R M R H U O T K L N C U S G I J J N Y W
N C O T M A R I Y O W T N D T M Q U T I
R I U A B U O T C A O I E I Y U R D I C
O T G N U F N S T A D P G M T M X L C H
V Y H A Y S N F C A E I K A S E M E E A
E I G G E G O I E K O S B C S Y D I K L
R A Q I L R T R P L U E N O A O E F O B
S H T W D Z S F O E G T X A D L R F T I
D B U R N L E Y R A S O A K W I B E S O
C O V E N T R Y C I T Y R F N S B H Z N
Q U E E N S P A R K R A N G E R S S A H
```

Birmingham City	Coventry City	Norwich City	Stoke City
Blackburn Rovers	Huddersfield Town	Preston North End	Sunderland
Blackpool	Hull City	Queens Park Rangers	Swansea City
Bristol City	Luton Town	Reading	Watford
Burnley	Middlesbrough	Rotherham United	West Bromwich Albion
Cardiff City	Millwall	Sheffield United	Wigan Athletic

46

ANSWERS ON PAGE 62

MARCELINO
NÚÑEZ

26

NORWICH CITY WOMEN FC

After England's fantastic achievement in winning the woman's UEFA European Championships in the summer of 2022, the profile of girl's and women's football continues to grow and grow.

Ahead of the new 2022/23 season, Norwich City's own women's team welcomed many new faces to the squad for their FA Women's National League South East Division One campaign.

After a rollercoaster 2021/22 season which saw the Norwich side finish in eighth place, just two points above the drop zone, the club have really strengthened their set-up both on and off the pitch for 2022/23.

Off the pitch the Canaries appointed Norfolk-born Flo Allen, a former full-time professional with Bristol City Woman, as the club's new general manager.

With the women's first team under the management of Shaun Howes, the club will look to grow the women's game at all levels from their base at The Nest while providing a development pathway for young girls to benefit from.

Having seen Norfolk-born Lauren Hemp star in the Lionesses' summer success, the quest is on to find the next international star while growing the women's game in Norwich and Norfolk.

The team primarily play their home games on a Sunday at the Norwich City Community Sports Foundation's impressive facility at The Nest where new supporters are always welcome.

Full details of the Norwich City women's team and their 2022/23 fixtures can be found on the club's official website canaries.co.uk

Bryony Williams	GK	Rebecca Russell	MF
Hope Armstrong	GK	Katie Knights	MF
Chardonnay Johnston	DF	Freya Symonds	MF
Summer Ward	DF	Betty Booker	MF
Alice Parker	DF	Leilah Gooding	MF
Katie Lee	DF	Jodie Drake	MF
Anna Larkins	DF	Megan Todd	FW
Naomi Cooper	DF	Natasha Snelling	FW
Jess Harper	DF	Rosie George	FW
Ceri Flye	DF	Kathryn Stanley	FW
Kate Parsons	DF	Holly Williams	FW
Millie Daviss	DF	Ella Gambell	FW
Ellie Smith	MF	Olivia Cook	FW

4. WHO AM I?

1. WHO AM I?

3. WHO AM I?

2. WHO AM I?

5. WHO AM I?

WHO? ARE YER ?

Can you figure out who each of these Norwich stars is?

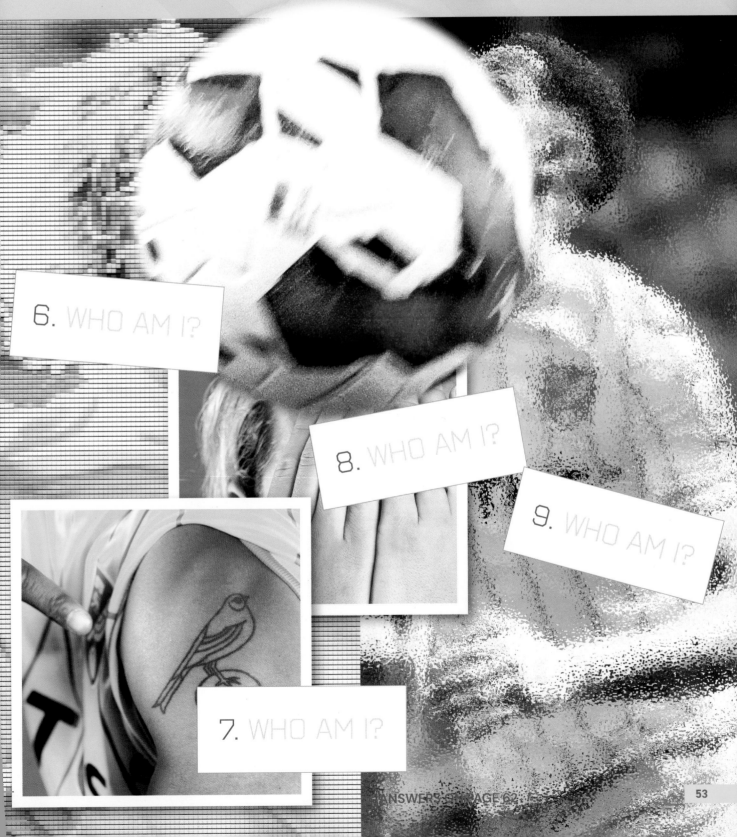

6. WHO AM I?

8. WHO AM I?

9. WHO AM I?

7. WHO AM I?

ANSWERS ON PAGE 62

TRUE COLOURS

Colour in
this picture of
Jacob Sørensen

PREMIER LEAGUE CHAMPIONS

LIVERPOOL

FAST FORWARD >>

Do your predictions for 2022/23 match our own?...

CHAMPIONSHIP WINNERS

NORWICH CITY

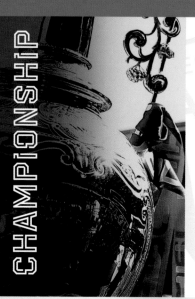

CHAMPIONSHIP

CHAMPIONSHIP RUNNERS-UP

WBA

PREMIER LEAGUE RUNNERS-UP

CHELSEA

PREMIER LEAGUE

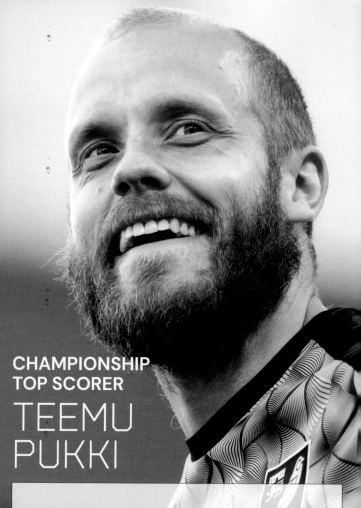

PREMIER LEAGUE TOP SCORER

ERLING HAALAND

CHAMPIONSHIP TOP SCORER

TEEMU PUKKI

LEAGUE ONE TOP SCORER
JAMES COLLINS

FA CUP WINNERS
SPURS

LEAGUE CUP WINNERS
LEICESTER CITY

LEAGUE ONE CHAMPIONS
DERBY COUNTY

CHAMPIONS LEAGUE WINNERS
REAL MADRID

LEAGUE ONE RUNNERS-UP
OXFORD UNITED

EUROPA LEAGUE WINNERS
ROMA

NUMBER OF SEASONS WITH THE CANARIES:

12

NORWICH CITY APPEARANCES:

477

NORWICH CITY GOALS:

0

PLAYER OF THE SEASON:

1987/88
1992/93

LEGEND

BRYAN GUNN

NORWICH CITY ACHIEVEMENTS:

FA Cup semi-finalists 1988/89. Third place Premier League finish 1992/93.

MAJOR STRENGTH:

Boasting supreme confidence with the ball at his feet, Gunn's ability to adjust to the back-pass rule in 1992/93 was a real asset to the Canaries.

INTERNATIONAL ACTION:

Bryan won all of his six full caps for Scotland as a Norwich City player.

FINEST HOUR:

A sensational display to protect Norwich's UEFA Cup lead against Bayern Munich in the Olympic Stadium in October 1993.

Norwich City has a long and proud history of fielding excellent goalkeepers and both Bryan Gunn and Rob Green have starred between the posts for the Canaries.

As the last line of defence, both Gunn and Green produced a host of match-winning saves throughout their Carrow Road careers while marshalling the defensive unit in front of them.

While Gunn proved to be an inspired signing, Green of course progressed though the youth ranks, but who was the best? It's a tricky one to decide and here are a number of facts and figures from their time at Carrow Road to help you reach your decision...

Yet again, it's a really a tough call!

NUMBER OF SEASONS WITH THE CANARIES:

8

NORWICH CITY APPEARANCES:

241

NORWICH CITY GOALS:

0

PLAYER OF THE SEASON:

Amazingly, Rob Green was never a winner of the Player of the Season award.

LEGEND

ROB GREEN

NORWICH CITY ACHIEVEMENTS:

Nationwide First Division Play–Off finalists (2001/02)...
Nationwide Division One title winners (2003/04).

MAJOR STRENGTH:

Great ability to thwart strikers in one-on-one situations.

INTERNATIONAL ACTION:

In the summer of 2005, Green became only the sixth Norwich City player to be capped by England.

FINEST HOUR:

Rob marked his debut as a teenager with a clean sheet in the white-hot atmosphere of an East Anglian derby match against Ipswich Town in April 1999 and that confident display set the tone for his impressive Canary career.

IDENTIFY THE STAR

Can you put a name to the football stars in these ten teasers?

GOOD LUCK...

ANSWERS ON PAGE 62

1. Manchester City's title-winning 'keeper Ederson shared the 2021/22 Golden Glove award for the number of clean sheets with which Premier League rival?

2. Which Portuguese superstar re-joined Manchester United in the 2021/22 season?

3. Can you name the Brazilian forward who joined Aston Villa in May 2022 following a loan spell at Villa Park?

4. Who became Arsenal manager in 2019?

5. Who scored the winning goal in the 2021/22 UEFA Champions League final?

6. After 550 games for West Ham United, which long-serving midfielder announced his retirement in 2022?

7. Who took the mantle of scoring Brentford's first Premier League goal?

8. Who scored the final goal for Manchester City in their 2021/22 Premier League title-winning season?

9. Which player had Squad No.35 at Carrow Road during 2021/22?

10. Who joined the Canaries from Everton in the summer of 2020?

ONEL HERNÁNDEZ

25

61

ANSWERS

PAGE 26 · TRUE OR FALSE

1. False (Harry played on loan for Leyton Orient, Millwall, Norwich City & Leicester City). **2.** True.
3. False (it was called Maine Road). **4.** True.
5. False (Gareth succeeded Sam Allardyce). **6.** True.
7. False (Jordan began his career at Sunderland).
8. True. **9.** True. **10.** False (it was from open play v Wolverhampton Wanderers).

PAGE 28 · CLASSIC FAN'TASTIC

PAGE 42 · MULTIPLE CHOICE

1. C. **2.** B. **3.** A. **4.** B. **5.** C.
6. A. **7.** B. **8.** B. **9.** B. **10.** C.

PAGE 46 · CLUB SEARCH

Huddersfield Town.

PAGE 48 · NAME THE SEASON

1. 2020/21.   **2.** 2012/13.   **3.** 1965/66.
4. 2021/22.   **5.** 2015/16.   **6.** 2020/21.
7. 2018/19.   **8.** 2011/12.   **9.** 2021/22.
10. 2014/15.

PAGE 49 · WHICH BALL?

Top. Ball H.   **Bottom.** Ball I.

PAGE 52 · WHO ARE YER?

1. Teemu Pukki. **2.** Josh Sargent. **3.** Grant Hanley.
4. Sam McCallum. **5.** Isaac Hayden. **6.** Todd Cantwell.
7. Onel Hernández. **8.** Todd Cantwell.
9. Andrew Omobamidele.

PAGE 60 · IDENTIFY THE STAR

1. Allison Becker (Liverpool). **2.** Cristiano Ronaldo.
3. Philippe Coutinho. **4.** Mikel Arteta.
5. Vinícius Júnior. **6.** Mark Noble. **7.** Sergi Canós.
8. İlkay Gündoğan. **9.** Adam Idah. **10.** Kieran Dowell.